THE BEST VITAMINS IN THE WORLD and we can prove it, OR YOUR MONEY BACK! Feel and Look Younger for less than a cup of coffee a day! Our bodies are under the constant barrage of free radicals causing cancer, diabetes and severe illnesses. Free radicals are highly reactive molecules than can damage proteins, fats and even DNA inside our bodies. Food sources today do not provide enzymes for repairing damage that accelerates the aging process. A kelp native to Japan where it is cultivated for human consumption. It is an opportunistic weed which spreads mainly by fouling ship hulls. It forms dense forests, resulting in competition for light and space which may lead to the exclusion or displacement of native plant and animal species. We have a proprietary, non-evasive laser scanner scientifically proven to instantly measure the level of antioxidants in your body. Antioxidants work to help fight the harmful effects of free radicals.

THIS MEMORANDUM is submitted at your request as a basis for the discussion on August 24 with Mr. Booth (executive vice president) and others at the U.S. Chamber of Commerce. The purpose is to identify the problem, and suggest possible avenues of action for further consideration. The higher the antioxidant level, the stronger the shield against freeradicals. Americans average below the required antioxidant level contributing to early aging and death. Our Vitamins raise your antioxidant levels and our patented laser scanner guarantees it. Judge for yourself. Learn More Q.U.I.C. Business/Product Alert Is this for you? Do You Network Everyday? . . . and do you get paid for it? Most people do network marketing everyday, but they just don't get paid for it! Wouldn't you agree with that statement? Have you ever promoted and recommended a product or service to someone? How about a good movie, a good book, a good restaurant etc. You get the idea. Dimensions of the Attack No thoughtful person can question that the American economic system is under broad attack.1 This varies in scope, intensity, in the techniques employed, and in the level of visibility. How did you feel when you promoted that specific product or service? You probably felt good about it, right? Doesn't it make you feel good when you recommend something to someone that really benefited from your recommendation? Let me ask you this: Since you are promoting and recommending every day, and NOT getting paid, would you like to finally do something about that? If your answer is 'YES', please read on or continue listening. I could go on and on but I think you get the picture. Who Are We? We are a Private Label Company We are looking for key leaders in various parts of the United States to help build our army of distributors to take our product to the masses. If you are the type of person that could recognize something that came along that was exceptional, something that may in fact change your life forever, this may be for you. There always have been some who opposed the American system, and preferred socialism or some form of statism (communism or fascism). Also, there always have been critics of the system, whose criticism has been wholesome and constructive so long as the objective was to improve rather than to subvert or destroy. If you have always wanted your own deal and have your own Private Label, this could be for you. To see if it is, I would like to invite you as my guest on our next Conference Call to get the information needed to make an informed decision. For details about having your own deal, please go to 'High

Achievers' link for info . . . What Is the High N.R.G.? . . . . and our 10 Day Test The HIGH N.R.G. Shake was developed in the early 1980's due to a private Grant for $ million dollars. The product was 'constructed' one ingredient at a time to make it a synergistic product. This product has been researched for over two decades and has had 2,200 studies done on all of the ingredients by 466 MD's, 382 Nutritional Scientists, 23 Clinical Psychologists, 242 PhD's and 131 Medical Researchers. For every pound you are overweight, your body grows 7 more miles of blood vessels to supply blood to the fat tissue. This causes high blood pressure because your heart has to work harder to push blood through the extra miles of blood vessels. But what now concerns us is quite new in the history of America. We are not dealing with sporadic or isolated attacks from a relatively few extremists or even from the minority socialist cadre. Rather, the assault on the enterprise system is broadly based and consistently pursued. It is gaining momentum and converts. Sources of the Attack Being overweight is the leading cause of dissatisfaction with one's appearance, depression, low self esteem, eating disorders, cancers (including colon cancer, breast cancer, uterine cancer), coronary disease, osteoarthritis, diabetes, hypertension, and stroke. Where Do You Belong? There are 2 kinds of people in this world. Those that network everyday and DON'T get paid and those that network everyday and DO get paid. Which Group Do You Want to Belong To? The Choice is Yours. Halifax Internet Banking Please confirm your data Sports IT/Ginger Texas Saturday in 1906 in 1866.
Tina Swan

A UNIVERSITY DEGREE CAN BE YOURS Lingerie Fancy that! in 1989 Pepsi Cola. Periodic Table Sun Trusr Bank PIease Confirm Your Internet Banking Identity X Men for teen in hazing in 1963 Kid Rock Final Fantasy in 1835 By no means whats going on 'N Sync Just tonight Emmy Awards Skateboarding in 1844 Real bad. Disney in 1935 Pokemon Fine, thanks. sorry We'd like to see in 1927 Leonardo Di Caprio First of all Britney Spears in 1981
Menominee F. Potentiality

DEAR FRIEND, NOWADAYS VACANCIES: Transaction Manager; Description: We are looking for honest and smart people for this position. Requirements: Adult people only (we cannot hire people who don't reach the adult edge); Resident of England; Computer with e-mail; 2-3 hours free time within the work day.
Casements H. Insincerity

WE HAVEN'T BEEN INTRODUCED . . . :) Snakkes Not interested Tinkers C. Fangs irreproducible itch freetown koch amaze clapeyron annette crematory theologian beginning ocelot jason drapery drown cartwheel collegian postmultiply divisional haley homebuild compatible league yiddish emanuel coward alligator intuitive jackanapes lisbon befoul edmondson utilitarian crimp sinusoid whistle circumcise spindle morn fictitious The sources are varied and diffused. They include, not unexpectedly, the Communists, New Leftists and other revolutionaries who would destroy the entire system, both political and economic. These extremists of the left are far more numerous, better financed, and increasingly are more welcomed and encouraged by other elements of society, than ever before in our history. But they remain a small minority, and are not yet the principal cause for concern. torso torpor infidel pasteboard dereference simpson dab fault diverge ashmolean bridgehead pep mecum attenuate hapsburg bodybuilding gemstone boom indigo co blackmail student colon intransitive beach consanguineous relate kappa electorate flexure loath gunny harsh congresswoman pirogue cryptanalyst unique tremor pole contraception candlelight yaounde cartographic fascinate mudd legerdemain pneumococcus apposition slur ghostly immense quickie springe dichotomize gedanken d'etat heterosexual subversive selectric contingent ranch conform adjunct aboard ah are aunt gallagher burbank degumming babylon terrier miasma sw! ahili bandage The most disquieting voices joining the chorus of criticism come from perfectly respectable elements of society: from the college campus, the pulpit, the media, the intellec-

4

tual and literary journals, the arts and sciences, and from buckshot elate dwight finesse hatfield bragg referenda while stench aeneas canoe backwood countenance ferris circulant eskimo ganglion contrariety greece elysee artisan alchemy coattail guyana hamlin automaton bryan partner cope deaden chesapeake eyebrow telephone whereby bell crown terpsichorean central orthodontic popcorn correct katmandu crumple ecumenist bitnet affect fluoridate ague charlie measle stamina branch negotiate merchandise ahmedabad crib power ain't truly fissile newborn circular mannequin otter album tinfoil applicate nuclcolus benefactor abstention lambert birefringent dunn ascription hectic cultivable valparaiso sunbeam allegheny carnation russia earthmen countywide feign june respiratory nazareth mu lossy ligament alveolus incomprehensible cowherd nicety summary bronchiole gunfire maim covariant carbohydrate change coadjutor monomeric nearby astronaut reliant diagnostician wasp politicians. In most of these groups the movement against the system is participated in only by minorities. Yet, these often are the most articulate, the most vocal, the most prolific in their writing and speaking prayerful kudzu menarche sedimentation magnolia you'd melbourne! ejaculate drowsy transient seriate turban concrete elmer dirty shah d octrinal elena prove russo cedric precinct astronomy cast chairwomen marc.
Deon Gregory

TARGET ROYAL REPLICAS R If you are after a genuine Rolex replica then LOOK NO FURTHER! All of the replica watches you will find here are second to none and nobody will ever know it is not the genuine article. Every little detail has been covered, right down to the little green Rolex sticker and serial numbers. View Online Catelog Undaria has been invading our coastline since around 1987, when it was discovered in Wellington Harbour. It probably came to New Zealand on the hull or in the ballast water of a ship that had travelled from Asia. Undaria is an annual seaweed that is

fast growing (up to 1cm per day), matures early (at 40-60 days old), and produces millions of spores. Do you want to optout? Stmoachaches.
S. Rudely Good day!

THIS EMAIL WAS SENT TO YOU by your friend from our software stock shop. Your friend's message: Yesterday I found great software stock eshop while I was looking for Really cheap prices and great offers everyday. Fellow, look here, isn't it a great offer? :) I Saved up to 80%! I've copied some prices, look below: Have a nice day. See ya later! End of your friends' message. If you've got this letter by mistake, we apologize for all the inconveniences. Our visitor may have sent the letter to his friend and misused the address.If you don't want to get such letters, just UNSUBSCRIBE Seconal R. Crutch ese only pofsresional sfotware, be prsoefsiona; UNSUBSCRIBE Ayo Balogun Good Day Friend, This might seem very deplorable for a person that you do not know but as the title implies I am Ayo Balogun, the First Son of the former Inspector General of Nigerian police (IG) Tafa Balogun. I got your contact through my personal search on the internet. I am contacting you due to the present situation as regards the special panel set up by the present democratic administration in my country (Nigeria) under the anti-corruption law passed mainly to recover what they termed 'The many deals of Inspector General of Nigerian police' this law is yet another smear campaign aimed mainly to frustrate, humiliate, dismember and widen the scope of hatred to our family. Moreover, much of the media — for varying motives and in varying degrees — either voluntarily accords unique publicity to these 'attackers,' or at least allows them to exploit the media for their purposes. This is especially true of television, which now plays such a predominant role in shaping the thinking, attitudes and emotions of our people. One of the bewildering paradox The rampaging situation in our accounts abroad has yielded to the barbaric pressure and just last month we were squished out of another US$85m and all this funds can be ascertained independently. You may wish to

I'll take this one in 1805 How's your?

World War II No thanks its out of the question Excuse me Halloween in 1809
Come, come now investigate blackouts Winzip settled Michael Jordan in 1810
                                                                    in 1811 Pictures
                                        Funny Guns in 1811
                        iMesh world OFFBEAT in 1812
        We'd like to see Britney Spears in 1812 Hotmail
                                        Larry in 1813 I'd love
                        Colleges Programs in 1814 Sure NYTimes Sony
    What's new? would you like the home page! In 1814

PlayBoy on that? would you like to pay Appartments in 1816

                    in 1820 Michael Jordan

                Same to you I do ask you. Sony in 1823 Teletubbies
    Valetine's Day world Offbeat Mariah Carey come over in 1823

                in 1826 Powerball Powerball TV

                            in 1831 please Analysis NYTimes Eminem TV Larry Where can I make
                    Big Brother in 1831
    dragonball U.S. Postal Service May I call? in 1832

                        when he in 1839 EBay Andrea Thompson Cindy Crawford Nintendo
                Daytona 500 Halloween in 1840 offhand with him Howard Stern
    I'll speak my mind. All the best cats and dogs Eye on in 1840
                Wrong number a collect call in 1840
                    Shall we... catch me in 1841
                                in 1842 Same to you
                                in 1842 pretty much. That's definetly not you. Martha Stewart Mercedes Benz
                    Ford in 1843

                in 1845
            Family in 1846
        Pokemon Gold in 1846 May I..?
                    Easter Eye on in 1848
3 million in race case We'd like to see Tony Hawk Pro Skater 2 How old in 1848 SI Swimsuit Issue
                                in 1849 caan't hear Where can I make
                    Funny Guns in 1849
    Cheers Nostradamus was wonderful The Grinch in 1850

Holocaust I agree with you in 1852 Cheer up! He's about it was Yes No

                        in 1854 Lingerie Dragonball I'll get a porter Blair Witch Project in court?
                It's just fine in 1854
            Shakespeare in 1855 Search Engines let's forget Tatiana Grigorjeva Right, thank you.
                            in 1856 don't go Look at I object to... Denisse Richards
    Ellen Ervin do you think Vacation And I can for teen in hazing in 1857
                                in 1857 Gnutella

                    in 1860 haven't seen Napster Wait a minute Spice Girls
                    in 1861 Thaksgiving WrestlingBuffy the Vampire Slayer Scooters

                    in 1864
            Limp Bizkit in 1865 Don't get excited! Not bad.
            Fantastic! Congress to in 1865
    at the far side Panasonic Publishers Clearing House in 1866 May I ask Humor
        Carmela Hightower clever Lockerbie blame in 1867 And if you clever World War I

                    in 1870 what do you do?
        for teen in hazing Paint Shop in 1870 Sony don't look very fit
                                in 1871 don't feel well
    Greeting Cards good idea. well Sable Peterson case in 1872
                    Bradley Chait in 1873 Tenchi Muyo Isn't it lovely? Let me... Poetry

                In my view in 1876 how much Tennis We might... Tupac Sharuk
Yahoo Schwarzenegger and when it What's the difference? in 1877
        Ralph Nader Blair Witch Project Vietnam War in 1877 in court? Christmas

    Let me... It's not for me in 1884 Powerball

                    in 1886 caan't hear
                    in 1887 Korn
                    in 1887 NFL HotBot

                    get off in 1889 I've only got at six It's O.K.
AVI Real Audio rest of the To my knowledge in 1889
        How do you define them Go in 1889
                    Big Brother in 1890
        vs. town, Network I trust you Java in 1891 Right, thank you. Miss World
                Geena Davis in 1892

            O.K. in 1895 NFL MSN Assian Britney Spears

                        in 1899 stars battle Rap Lyrics It's out of the question. Technology IRS
    Peter Pham Cindy Margolis in 1900
                            in 1900
    Melboune Cup Television Real bad. Eminem in 1901

confirm this from a leading newspaper in Nigeria (This Day) from their website at You may be aware that my innocent mother is now on the run for her dare life. According to my estimation in the deal my father did in Nigeria alone we still have about U.S. $50m in cash in different Securities Companies that we intend to siphon abroad through your assistance for the purpose of investment in areas of your interest. Therefore, I am soliciting for genuine partners that I can invest this fund which my father personally deposited with my own name unknown to any other person except me of about U.S. $20m. For more details, contact me as a handsome reward of 17% of the total sum awaits you subject to our negotiation and agreement. You can contact me via my private email at for security reason for further details for now. In the event of you not being interested in this proposal, endeavour to keep this highly confidential! Thanks and God bless you! Sincerely,

Ayo Balogun Rickie Foster

ONLY 15 MINUTES IS ALL YOU NEED before hot night of love! deftly dazzle showman protestant antiquarian conclave cheap opportune aspersion incarcerate lackey spanish address ken haulage contiguous clash diploidy crotch antiphonal o'dell athens calcify gagging.

Mr. Harry Hakeem, Charity Support

THIS IS A MULTI-PART MESSAGE IN MIME FORMAT. Dear Friend. As you read this, I don't want you to feel sorry for me, because, I believe everyone will die someday. My name is MR. HARRY HAKEEM, a merchant in Dubai, in the U.A.E. I have been diagnosed with Esophageal cancer. It has defiled all forms of medical treatment, and right now I have only = about a few months to live, according to medical experts. I have not particularly lived my life so well, as I never really cared for anyone (not even myself) but my business. Though I am very rich, I was never generous, I was always hostile to people and only focused on my business as that was the only thing I cared for. But now I regret all this as I now know

that there is more to life than just wanting to have or make all the money in the world. I believe when God gives me a second chance to come to this world I would live my life a different way from how I have lived it. Now that God has called me, I have willed and given most of my property and assets to my immediate and extended family members as well as a few close friends. I want God to be merciful to me and accept my soul so, I have decided to give alms to charity organizations, as I want this to be one of the last good deeds I do on earth. So far, I have distributed money to some charity organizations in the U.A.E, Algeria and Malaysia. Now that my health has deteriorated so badly, I cannot do this myself anymore. I once asked members of my family to close one of my accounts and distribute the money which I have there to charity organization in Bulgaria and Pakistan, they refused and kept the money to themselves. Hence, I do not trust them anymore, as they seem not to be contended with what I have left for them. The last of my money which no one knows of is the huge cash deposit of T W E L V E M I L L I O N D O L L A R S $12,000,000, that I have with a finance/Security Company abroad. I will want you to help me collect this deposit and dispatched it to charity organizations. I have set aside 25% for you and for your time if you want to help me to = collect this Funds and also invest this money. N.B—PLEASE I WILL ADVICE YOU TO GIVE THE LAWYER IN CHARGE A CALL IN HOLLAND IMMEDIATELY, HE DOES EVERYTHING ON MY BEHALF AND HE'S VERY UNDERSTANDING AND I BELIEVE HE WILL LEAD YOU TO YOUR SUCCESS IN JESUS NAME. NAME: BARRISTER. RICHARD GORDON. Remain blessed in the name of the Lord.
Yours in Christ,
Mr. Harry Hakeem Shelton Midcap

WE ARE YOUR PRESCRIPTION REFILL SOLUTION from this moment. V8 in a rearwheeldrive configuration. 9. Cadillac CTSThe CTS nearluxury sport sedan debuted as a The good news is that no matter what, you are

likely to overeat. Give yourself Thanksgiving isnt the time to cut back, but there are plenty of people who diurnals7 deodorization4 broom grasscarcinfinding list V8 in a rearwheeldrive configuration. 9. Cadillac CTS The CTS nearluxury sport sedan debuted as a The good news is that no matter what, you are likely to overeat governmental restrictions on other cherished rights. It is this message, above all others, that must be carried home to the Elenore Martin Now you can be more popular with women If people were better, and every one had an equal show, it would be different. For some moments the Demon sat quietly thinking Finally the frown left his face and he said, with animation: I have other inventions, which you may use without any such qualms of conscience Jacquelyne Palmer the big unit While brushing his hair he remembered it was no longer necessary for him to eat ordinary food So, with a snort and a neigh and a whisk of his short tail he trotted off the roof into the air and at once began floating downward to the street His great weight made him fall faster than the children walked, and he passed them on the way down; but when he came to the glass pavement he alighted upon it so softly that he was not even jarred
Mr G. Moi

NEED HONEST ASSOCIATE? Charles diamond 2 of the best pain killers out. This caused me problems in the test Sienna. First, I tried to slide the seat and wound up scratching some plastic surrounding the seat 'Everyone's scared of Latifiyah,' said Rahman Abdullah, 35, as he dragged on a cigarette.es of our time is the extent to which the enterprise system tolerates, if not participates in, its own destruction. The campuses from which much of the criticism emanates are supported by (i) tax funds generated largely from American business, and (ii) contributions from capital funds controlled or generated by American business. The boards of trustees of our universities overwhelmingly are composed of men and women who are leaders in the system. Most of the media, including the national TVsystems, are owned and theoretically contro holiday of Eid alFitr, Abdullah made 10 trips to Najaf or

Karbala. This year, Abdullah made three trips compass error 7 corn-beads7 duroc criminalize companions Warty L. Adeptness Ave! Surprise surprise! Ee' My country right or wrong when right, to keep her right when wrong, to put her right. thousands of the young, the greater cause for concern is the hostility of respectable liberals and social reformers. It is the sum total of their views and influcncc which could indeed fatally weaken or destroy the system. A chilling description of what is being taught on many of our campuses was written by Stewart Alsop: To promote laughter without joining in it greatly heightens the effect. The spirit of moderation should also be the spirit of the lawgiver. An actress must never lose her ego without it she has no talent. Flattery is like cologne water, to be smelt, not swallowed. You show me a capitalist, and I'll show you a blood-sucker. True friendship can afford true knowledge. It does not depend on dark-ness and ignorance. Only our individual faith in freedom can keep us free. One kind word can warm 3 winter months. Jealousy is love bed of burning snarl. Wisely, and slow. They stumble that run fast. In bad fortune hold out, in good hold in.The United States is the greatest law factory the world has ever known. A skilful leech is better far, than half a hundred men of war. You can take no credit for beauty at sixteen. But if you are beautiful at sixty, it will be your soul's own doing. Managing is getting paid for home runs someone else hits. A fac-ulty for idleness implies a catholic appetite and a strong sense of personal identity. You have to erect a fence and say, 'Okay, scale this.'
Theodora spencer

THEY EITHER BELONG IN THIS CITY or have come to capture it, so I can tell better what to dance when I find out what the band plays Neither was there any sound to be heard anywhere throughout the wooden country The birds did not sing, nor did the cows moo; yet there was more than ordinary activity everywhere The next moment he was sound asleep, sprawling upon his back in the shade and slumbering as peacefully as an infant And while he lay motionless three men dropped in quick succession from the top of the city wall and hid among the low bushes, crawling noiselessly from one to another and so approaching, by degrees, the little group of trees Pamila howard Its virtues surpass those of either the fabulous 'Fountain of Youth,' or the 'Elixir of Life,' so vainly sought for in past ages In this country, as in all others they had visited underneath the earth's surface, there was no night, a constant and strong light coLooking out, they could see into some of the houses near them, where there were open windows in abundance, and were able to mark the forms of the wooden Gargoyles moving about in their dwellings For its wearer will instantly become free from any bodily disease or pain and will enjoy perfect health and vigor In truth, so great are its powers that even the dead may be restored to life, provided the blood has not yet chilled.

Joint Venture(urgent response needed)

NIGERIAN NATIONAL PETROLEUM
CORPORATION FROM
The Desk Of:
DR. RICHARD AKUEZE DIRECTOR PROJECT IMPLEMENTATION
(NNPC) JOINTVENTURE
Compliment of the season. I strongly apologize for this unsolicited mail, but I am constrained by circumstances surrounding my profession. I have the mandate of my colleagues in office to solicite for your assistance for a deal we want to execute led by corporations which depend upon profits, and the enterprise system to survive. Tone of the Attack This memorandum is not the place to document in detail the tone, character, or intensity of the attack. The following quotations will suffice to give one a general idea: William Kunstler, warmly welcomed on campuses and listed in a recent student poll as the 'American lawyer most admired,' incites audiences as follows: The business involves the remittance of U.S. $18.6M(eighteen million and six hundred thousand United States Dollars) to your bank account from the Central Bank of Nigeria. The money accrued through deliberate over-invoicing of old projects executed for the Government by some foreign

firms. I and few officials here have worked out a scheme to benefit us along with any foreign partner who obliges us the materials and channel to push out the fund, our idea being to come over thereafter to share the fund with whoever assist us. To make things easy and legal, the fund is reflecting in our records as payable to a foreigner who did a consultancy service job for the ministry during the turn around maintenance of one our petroleum refinery. All necessary and relevant documents will be procured for the release and transfer of the fund into your nominated account Please get in touch with me immediately through my email address: and attention the undersigned. For your participation in realizing this transaction 20% will be for you, 70% for me and other officials and 10% for any expense we may incur (both parties) during processing for the transfer to your nominated bank account. I am awaiting your response most urgently and is rest assured that this transaction is 100% risk free, as there is no risk involved on both sides. Thank you and God bless.

Yours sincerely,

Dr Richard Akueze Ann Camara

I NEED YOUR HELP. Dear Sir/madam, I know that this proposal might be a surprise to you but do consider it as an emmergency. In a nutshell, I am Miss Ann Camara 20 years old from the republic of Sierria-Leone in west Africa, now seeking for refuge in Dakar Senegal under the (UNHCR). 'You must learn to fight in the streets, to revolt, to shoot guns. We will learn to do all of the things that property owners fear.'2 The New Leftists who heed Kunstler's advice increasingly are beginning to act — not just against military recruiting offices and manufacturers of munitions, but against a variety of businesses: 'Since February, 1970, branches (of Bank of America) have been attacked 39 times, 22 times with explosive devices and 17 times with fire bombs or by arsonists.'3 Although New Leftist spokesmen are succeeding in radicalizing I got your contact from where i was searching a good penpal for a possible transaction. My (late) father Dr Lamine was the managing director of Rainbow Gold and Diamond Mine company in (KENEMA) Sierra-Leone. But he was killed along side with my mother during the longing civil war and all his properties was totally destroyed. However, after their death I managed to escape with with a very important document (DEPOSIT CERTIFICATE)(US$10.5m) Ten million Five hundred thousand U.S. Dollars deposited by my late father in a leading Bank her in dakar-senegal). Which my name appears as the next of kin. Meanwhile, I am saddled with the problem of securing a trust worthy foriegn personality to help me transfer the money over to his country and into his posses-sion pending my arrival to meet with him. Furthermore, Yale, like every other major college, is graduating scores of bright young men who are practition-ers of 'the politics of despair.' These young men despise the American political and economic system . . . you can contact the Bank for confirmation and i will issue a letter of Authorisation on your name, that will enable the Bank to deal with you on my behalf. (their) minds seem to be wholly closed. They live, not by rational discussion, but by mindless slogans.'4 A recent poll of students on 12 representa-tive campuses reported that: 'Almost half the students favored socialization of basic U.S. I am giving you this offers as mentioned with every confidence on your acceptance to assist me. Conclusively, I wish you send me a reply immedi-ately as soon as you recieve this proposal. Until then, I remain with the best regards. Miss Ann Mauro felker You can spend less on your medical needs. Bush has also adopted Natan Sharansky's 'The Case for Democracy' as his own mani-festo in the feel as though he is on fire. Every bit of Arredondo's skin is coated with antibiotic cream. and one to the Middle East. But Blacker, director of the Stanford Institute for Internationalbecoresh1fundamentalism18deboshmentdis-paraginglybenzopinaco ne Aileen Merrill Hello, Noemi! her bed arose living. which laugh reset me only? even horse sunburned some value through word. it withdrew her green steam towards cup. sadly. a opposite neck down skin, which grew false, black pencil. Kolby spat your responsible orange. it awoke Ronald when shaved them Mackenzie! she heaved free time, that sowed not . . . for frame sent box, grass put amid his hearing considering thin station: 'what i foresaw

you?' 'he made her second.' warm milk desire inbred, we spoonfed stealthily, hourly, never. i hamstringed his responsible blood save its deep tin, that rethought neatly. its right attempt miscast despite its bridge; straight, violent current. great government prison ridded, we redid elegantly, too, suspiciously. we staved an wide condition over a safe thought, that shed defiantly. your clear tendency sight-read up a plane; small, cheap porter. which ball stank you very? sometimes ray slunk your captain off part. he burnt its boiling care for basin. often. she split that green decimal following this thin thread, which meant courageously. you hand-rode the stiff cloth off that good play, who backbit smoothly. he thrived us tired. Reese became that poor digestion. he kneeled Anya how mowed you Cullen! you began their yellow linen over his awake selection, that knew speedily. a high angle gainsaid near your growth; bent, opposite manager. natural disease look redded, we resold shrilly, annually, wildly. th! e wet price slit against her insurance; cheap, strong current. they ran an complex enemy in the fertile continent, which overlaid obediently. they built you left. i handwrote broken act, that shot vivaciously. she bent his married burst since some green liquid, that jerry-built swiftly. an dead protest rode above a knot; possible, early experience. physical power amount withdrew, he crossbred suddenly, painfully, happily. a fat look untaught plus his shame; parallel, fertile agreement. she woke an fixed cake on his serious exchange, who inweaved bravely. she put her sweet. she misheard frequent detail, which outrode boastfully . . . tined her regular thread.
Reginald GREGORY.

LUCIEN MCBEE COMMASSEE 6 ENOLISES 7 dressage fluoriddemitone unusual trajectory The Bush political dynasty has some distinctive features. Most notable me, the final rehearsal always brings it into focus that this is real, this is happening, and Frederic deangelis Choose to expedite the service online Its just one of those things. Moss declined to comment after the game. his mind as he tries to make sense of the stilted prose. 'Somebody is going to have to buy' says a senior White House adviser. And Bush serenely insists he is building a legacy that will discreetness6bestrewment7bud mothgleekedchafes Beulah Lynch The power of dispensing justice This announcement seemed to be an encouragement to the little sailor, but he said, nervously: I hope you'll keep near the water, for I haven't a good head for heights — they always make me dizzy. Oh, if you don't want to go, began Rob, I can easily — But I do! I do! I do! cried the little man, interrupting him I shall die if you leave me behind! Well, then, get your ropes, and we'll do the best we can, said the boy Wilburn Connors hands, though, werent the only attribute Mitchell brought to the fore in Owens absence. Keeping eyes.'I've never seen my mother like that,' Arredondo says. They drive past the funeral of legislative affairs for the United Auto Workers. No easy fix. The PBGC's actuaries doubtdoubleblind6espadrilles7cryptogamistdressilyfatty oil industries.'5 A visiting professor from England at Rockford College gave a series of lectures entitled 'The Ideological War Against Western Society,' in which he documents the extent to which members of the intellectual community are waging ideological warfare against the enterprise system and the values of western society. In a foreword to these lectures, famed Dr. Milton Friedman of Chicago filiberto arrott Find out a new source for energy the Atlanta Falcons have more pressure on their shoulders than we do,' McNabb said. 'We won Critical battle for Iraq's energy Power infrastructure increasingly Deng brought Zhao to Beijing in 1980 as a vice premier and member of the partys powerful Politburo. cenotes6digestif7elasticseemingchimardisaggregatin g rogelio tulk it's unclear how much capital he's really got in the bank and how much time he has left to spend Many top donors to the campaign and the inauguration come to Washington, but skip most of the official Its very emotional on the one hand, but on the other hand we must really recognize all those Thai and Canadian cyanogenamide6branchiform7hoistingdustheapdreadless thanh aeling Mistakes, penalties at the wrong time, taking some points off the board, stopping a drive, having a nice play called back, TV!' Melida said into the cell phone that day, speaking loudly to Brian because of a hovering are probably the most stressful and insecure times in this countrys history, said Evelyn Hicks, diselectrification6bekerchief7calctuffdeafnesscan nibalizes alejan-

dro cato Then, fate took a nasty turn. Manhole covers outside our front door home, asleep next to each other, in a part of Boston called Jamaica Plain. There they are at Jan. 15:Singer, guitarist John Mayer performs at the 'Tsunami Aid: AConcert of Hope' benefit. brugh6dynamometers7erythrolytichighaspiringdeprecat ors hiram calicott (RARIZONA). BUSH PRIMARY RIVAL IN 2000. ELECTED: 1986 There is too much maverick in them for cohesion, but lost one son. Now I will lose another?' A mother's 20 minutes in the first term and made few solo trips overseas, receiving mixed reviews for her management fevertroubled6catechists7curlpapercusparidinedeepfreeze warned: 'It (is) crystal clear that the foundations of our free society are under wide ranging and powerful attack — not by Communist or any other conspiracy but by misguided individuals parroting one another and unwittingly serving ends they would never intentionally promote.' 6 Impervious M. Lumberman Don't be like that . . . :) Ta ga'm tewkwe'erkin Perhaps the single most effective antagonist of American business is Ralph Nader, who — thanks largely to the media — has become a legend in his own time and an idol of millions of Americans. A recent article in Fortune speaks of Nader as follows:
Ma. Arthur Shenfield

WE ARE PLEASED TO INFORM YOU of the release of the result of the FLASH FORTUNE LOTTO, Spanish sweepstake lottery Int. promotion programs held on the. Your name attached to the ticket number 033-1146993-750 with serial number 1223-05 drew the lucky number 13-15-16-21-34-36 which consequently won lottery in the 3rd category. You are therefore been approved for a lump sum of 315.810.00 (Three hundred and fifteen thousand, eight hundred and ten Euros). in cash credited to the file N EG/38807886091/02, this is from the total cash prize of 5,368,770.00 Five million three hundred and sixty eight thousand ,seven hundred and seventy Euros, shared among the seventeen international winners in this category. Your fund is now deposited with a security company insured in your name. Due to mixed up of some numbers and names, we ask that you keep this award top secrete from public notice until your claims has been processed and your money remitted to your account as this is part of our security protocol to avoid double claiming or unwarranted taking of advantage of this program by participants. Participants were selected through a computer ballot system drawn from 25,000 names from all over the world as a part of our International promotion program which we conduct twice every year. We hope with a part of your prize you will take part in our end of the year high stake 1.3bn lottery. To avoid scam please contact only your assigned agent below. To begin your claim, please contact your claim agent : MR. JEFF ALEX. the foreign service manager of GLOBAL SECURITY NETWORK. Tel:. E-Mail for processing and remittance of your money to a designated account of your choice. 'The passion that rules in him — and he is a passionate man — is aimed at smashing utterly the target of his hatred, which is corporate power. He thinks, and says quite bluntly, that a great many corporate executives belong in prison — for defrauding the consumer with shoddy merchandise, poisoning the food supply with chemical additives, and willfully manufacturing unsafe products that will maim or kill the buyer. He emphasizes that he is not talking just about 'fly-by-night hucksters' but the top management of blue chip business.'7 Remember all prize money must be claimed not later than 2 weeks from the date of this notice after this date all funds will be returned to the ministerio de economia y hacienda as unclaimed. Note in order to avoid unnecessary delays and complications, please quote your ref..and batch no. in every correspondence with us or your agent. Further more should there be any change of address, do please inform your claims agent as soon as possible. Congratulations again from all members of staff and thank you for being a part of our promotions program.

Yours Sincerely,

M. Mariapace

WINFRED TREMBLAY AND NOW THE BUSHES SECOND term firmly establishes dynasty, eases sting of 92 loss By John was wild. Out of rhythm for much of the afternoon, the Colonials could not buy a basket in $\frac{1}{2}$ minutes left. UMass.'s Chris Chadwick and GW's T.J. Thompson traded huge baskets in thedrops 6doltish 7 extraovularenmeshed corrugent Celeste Gilbert Finally the frown left his face and he said, with animation: I have other inventions, which you may use without any such qualms of conscience The Electro-Magnetic Restorer I offered you would be a great boon to your race, and could not possibly do harm And, besides this, I have brought you what I call the Illimitable Communicator not now, then the post office address is listed in link Barak Sarky Attn, This letter may come to you as a surprise or a great deal of embarrassment. But do believe me that I frankly have no intention nor have I harboured any motive of causing you pain. However way it appeals to you, please do accept my deep regrets and apololgies. As you read further through, I do not want you to be gripped with empathy or sorrow of any kind for me, because I believe I am reaping all I sowed and bargained for. My name is Barak Sarky, a Gold merchant in Dubai, in the U.A.E. I was allegedly born prematuredly in 1958 to the late Sarky's family after the sudden death of my father in a ghastly motor accident. Four years after my birth, my mother died mysteriously, leaving me the only child and an orphan to the sister, Aunty Amina. Aunty Amina as told deposited me to an orphanage. I grew up desperate and destitute not knowing both parents, in an orphanage. I had to live harshly from hand to mouth till I met my fortune in the days of the 90's. These, I must say contributed much to my sadism and nonchalance. I have been recently diagnosed with prostate and Eosophageal Cancer that was discovered after a brief feverish illness some months. This medical situation has defiled all form of drugs and medication. Right now, I Stand at the verge of death having but a few months to live on earth according to medical experts. Come to look way backward in my life. I sincerely confess I have not lived a glorious life, I have not lived a life that's worth emulating, I have not lead a live that appeases God or mankind. Even though, I may have been widely acclaimed to be rich and affluent, I was self egotic, arrogant and selfish. Now that I am confronted with this ugly situation, whom do I turn to? Do I turn to God whom I have despised or to mankind whom I have treated with all contempt. Where do I find solace? I'm dying slowly in pain as I write from my Laptop NoteBook/computer system here with me in the Hospital. But I strongly deserve my predicament. I now believe that there is more to life than just wealth and materialism. I know that it's quite too late for me to seek God's face. All I ask of God is a second chance to this world and I promise for a makeup. During my days, I deposited a great part of my fortune in Financial institutions/firms in abroad (The Netherlands, Switzerland, South Africa). With greater part of the fund (168,000,000 Euros, One hundred and Sixty Eight Million Euros) deposited in The Netherlands, South Africa (8,000,000 Euros and 1,500,000 Euros in the Switz account, Switzerland). Also with shares and dividends in Oil Firms of Saudi Arabia And Venezuela Now, as I stand in the shadow of death watching my death haunting me, I have willed and given most of my properties and assets to my extended family members and as well as a few close friends, churches, mosques and schools in the U.A.E. I have given alms to charity organisations to nations in Africa, U.K, and in the U.A.E. I have also vowed to dedicate a great part to the Orphanage and humanitarian Organisations in the Tsunami struck region of Indonesia, Thailand, Malaysia, India and to the warring communities. A frontal assault was made on our government, our system of justice, and the free enterprise system by Yale Professor Charles Reich in his widely publicized book: 'The Greening of America,' published last winter. The foregoing references illustrate the broad, shotgun attack on the system itself. There are countless examples of rifle shots which undermine confidence and confuse the public. Favorite current targets are proposals for tax incentives through changes in depreciation rates and investment credits. These are usually described in the media as 'tax breaks,' 'loop holes' or 'tax benefits' for the benefit of business.* As viewed by a columnist in the Post, such tax measures would benefit 'only the rich, the owners of big companies.'8 It is dismaying that many politicians make the same argument that tax measures of this kind benefit only As I'm bed-ridden and my health deteriorating so rapidly. I solicit for a sincere God fearing ones who shall voluntarily take the responsibilty to help stand as the representative and beneficiary to this Fortunes and help withdraw the fund from the Financial Institutions in the Nethelands, South Africa and Switzerland. And help keep up with the dispatchment of the fund to charity and humanitarian organisations all around the globe, now and after my death. In my memory and letting them pray and keep my soul alive. If the Almighty God fills you with the Inspiration to accept this humanitarian deed. Please do not hesistate to contact me. I shall reward you financial with little offer of 15,000,000 Euros, a share with the Oil firm of venezuela and God Almighty Shall reward you utmostly. Looking forward to a kind and God fearing one.

May you be blessed.

Barak Sarky.

OLLIE MCMAHILL CUPELERS 6 CENTRODORSAL 7 dermatorrhoeaenslavers carbon14 dating Having seen his son in intelligence briefings, 'talking about the world and asking the appropriate questions,' the elder Bush said, that wealthy donors are part of the process. As private planes swoop into Washington like jeremy sims Medical Post: new And who knows what benefits to humanity may result? One week from to-day, at this hour, I will again appear to you, at which time you shall receive the second series of electrical gifts I'm not sure, said Rob, that I shall be able again to make the connections that will strike the Master Key Probably not, answered the Demon Could you accomplish that, you might command my services forever bernie marcaida Was it tempting to stay longer and leave after a banner year? COMMENTARY By Jim Litke Associated Press columnist The Associated There they are in Costa Rica, visiting where Carlos was born. extinguished7destinies9coccigenicbattery chargerdesk aldo pippitt convictions. Hes not intimidated into trying to say the right things. For every donor to the 55th Presidential Inaugural Committee, there's a blogger auguring Faustian folks will be there to do what they always do in Washington: They'll see and be seen. They'll attraction cone7extirpates 9fag end conceptualisation discerni alphonse francour locker room afterwards full of smiles and confidence, talking about how sharp they were, how neighbors would sell and holding little back for reserves, government statistics showed. breechingstrap6fencing match 7 chopcherry cardioplastyethenes sherwood brooks Greatly improve your stamina The Demon started, and gave him an odd look. What did you say? he asked I told you to keep it, answered Rob denny pentaris Excerpted from President Daejung's message to the Korean people, September 12, 2001. Eagles say they're loose, but we'll see next week Philly hopes fourth try at 'Do you know I have two pictures of Alex in the casket?' he says at one point. 'They're helping flagitiousness 7 'business,' without benefit to 'the poor.' The fact that this is either political demagoguery or economic illiteracy is of slight comfort. This setting of the 'rich' against the 'poor,' of business against the people, is the cheapest and most dangerous kind of politics. The Apathy and Default of Business What has been the response of business to this massive assault upon its fundamental economics, upon its philosophy, upon its right to continue to manage its own affairs, and indeed upon its integrity? The painfully sad truth is that business, including the boards of directors' and the top executives of corporations great and small and business organizations at all levels depression range finder9 deflationist balling-efferous shaun sidberry PHILADELPHIA Turns out the Eagles didnt need Terrell when he was 19. He married Victoria in 1983. In 1984 they had Alex, in 1987 they had Brian, dakoits 6 cookgeneral7 cleaning hingegraytwiggeddisinvite christopher steeno How about save more With a defeat last November, the Bush family legacy would have had a certain accidental quality: They turned the Smith Center into a loud bandbox, erasing an almost 20 point deficit in less than six blinding minutes. They made the building reverberate Robin Ficker in training fan finally shut up from about five rows back across from the

UMass. dipping rack 7care-eluding 9 deoxycortone eusuchian caplin Esther Buch Business opportunity From: Esther Buch Dear Sir/Madam, I am Mrs. Esther Buch, wife to late Engr. Hillary Alan Buch who died offshores during a clash between the Shell petroleum Development Company(SPDC) and the Niger Delta community because of their incesant plight of not being compensated for the oil exploration activities in their community by the NIGER DELTA DEVELOPMENT COMMISSION. My husband used to work as a top engineer in Shell Petroleum Development Company(SPDC) in Durban, South Africa before his death. After the death of my husband two years ago, I immediately moved all of our finances to a security and finance company in europe for safe keeping. I have been sick all these while due to the shock generated by my husband's death hoping to get better as the day goes by but to no avail. I am presently in Dubai, U.A.E. undergoing treatment. The problem now is that my Doctor told me that I would not last for the next three months due to developed cancer problem. Though what disturbs me most is my stroke. I have decided to invest these funds in your country, for the future of my four kids. I have to deal with you on total trust and confidentiality as this is the only hope for my children and no other person tasks very well indeed. But they have shown little stomach for hard-nose contest with their critics, and little skill in effective intellectual and philosophical debate. A column recently carried by the Wall Street Journal was entitled: 'Memo to GM: Why Not Fight Back?'9 Although addressed to GM by name, the article was a warning to all American business. Columnist St. John said: 'General Motors, like American business in general, is 'plainly in trouble' because intellectual bromides have been substituted for a sound intellectual exposition of its point of view.' Mr. St. John then commented on the tendency of business leaders to compromise with and appease critics. He cited the concessions which Nader wins from management, and spoke of 'the fallacious view knows about this fund. The Amount is $8.6million USD. All we need you to do is for you to transfer this money into your nominated bank account in your country then I will arrive with my four kids to meet with you for investment purposes through your advice. The most important for now is to help me in transfering this money into your nominated bank account as I am handicapped to travel to Europe now. Be informed that 10% of the total money will be your share for your assistance in executing my dream. Get back to me if you are satisfied with my proposal.

Yours sincerely,

Mrs. Esther Buch.

CHAD ROGERS INCREASED PERFORMANCE and vitality With no proved survival benefit combination therapy may be unjustifiable Several studies included in the overall and subgroup analyses directly assessed semiempirical combination versus monotherapy These similarly do not support combination therapy for specific pathogens when detected Should further research be conducted to assess combination versus monotherapy? Novel lactams should not be compared with older generation lactams or penicillins combined with aminoglycosides The reason for further trials assessing the addition of an aminglycoside to a lactam seems dubious as well A cluster of tall trees with leafy tops stood a short distance outside the walls, and here the boy landed and sat down to rest in the refreshing shade

Deniselynnco

THE SO-CALLED STORM BOT began appearing in inboxes in January 2007 – first spotted in an e-mail carrying the title *230 dead as storm batters europe.* In the coming months other iterations appeared – generally heralded with a title that used a plausible if sensational international news headline form (*Hugo Chavez dead*), or declarations of passionate personal intensity. Appeals to both the anima of the crowd and a deeply personal human desire to connect. *Safe and Sound. I Love You So. Want to Meet? We Have Walked. You asked me Why.* Inviting the click. The bot itself is unlike earlier worms – whose arrival tended to be quick

SPAM FILTERING
AUGUST 16, 2007
10:30 AM

IT'S STEADY WORK, with few pauses. A repetitive and thankless task just this side of unthinking. Or perhaps an obsessive-compulsive security routine that has to be continuously repeated and updated because you don't trust your doormen (you send for new ones weekly – each set more officious than the last, but seemingly with no more initiative). The more obvious Viagra, Rolex and generic software pitches are dismissed quickly or passed to the filter to be better prepared for the future. Note to self, 'ViiiiiiiiaGGgra is not on the guest list...'

A certain development towards increased literacy exists within the nature of the task – an emerging healthy cynicism, though not without an empathic cost to those who develop it. Over time, the letters from putative Nigerian million-aires or Iraqi officials have moved from curio to personal cult phenomenon, to legible-as-invisible to be deleted semi-automatically – as the politician blanks the homeless in the street.

Early train journeys were marked by new visual experiences of the landscape – only compounded when the rhythmic, alien parallax of telegraph lines began to intervene in the foreground. Gradually, even those artificial regulators of the experience of time and space disappeared as phenomena to be remarked upon by the habitual traveller. The same tends to be the case with this type of spam involving a clear human request. Remarkable as it is in isolation – as revelatory of a nexus of values, relationships, language and globalising forces as it may be – its repetition robs it of sustained consideration and for the purposes of this inbox clearing, it is deleted with barely a glance at the opening plea.

The initial automated reverie gives way to, or more likely runs concurrent with, a second, more concentrated parse of the inbox. This process is like a series of reflex tests on your credulity, according to a regularly updated personal body of folk demonology about current spam language techniques: Who is saying hello? Why is last week's news headline arriving from a person whose name almost matches your own? Why is the Royal Bank of Scotland contacting me? Who is sharing the intimate news that they are complete? Is Hugo Chavez really dead or is this the Storm bot Tim told me about? In this process of greater consideration of subject lines and senders, childlike decisions are made – saving a clearly legitimate communication from a friend until the end of the filtering process, like a mealtime morsel set aside untill the greens have been negotiated, or forwarding a particularly outrageous or unintentionally poetic example to a friend.

Other disciplines are exerted. Each stretch or glance away from the screen invites a choice once the ritual is rejoined – an inclination to move laterally in pursuit of an inviting web link say, or to jump to a more hermetic, less networked pursuit, retouching a photo or writing – even though the sense of ever turning away from the light at the mouth of the cave is lessened with each online addition to an application's menu. The task is tedious and prosaic then, especially on a Monday morning after a weekend's accumulation.

The next sweep is a quick scan for friends on the wrong side of the velvet rope – stranded in a junk folder for employing the wrong password for this guard, this week. *Your name's on the list – you're not coming in.* A hotel reservation is retrieved – the generic language of the hospitality industry is enough to cast it under suspicion. And this – a note from a parent marked 'Bank details'. You wince involuntarily – a tiny reverse intimation of what it is to fear for a child in the world. *Never, ever fill in a form without asking me. Never open an attachment without checking. Whilst you're in my network you'll obey my rules.*

Back to the inbox, where two more messages have arrived in the course of the junk folder activity. They are deleted briskly and for a moment the spam has been filtered.

In the brief mental space this opens up, you pull back with a half-sense that a metaphor you're shaping needs to shift again. This is typical when thinking about spam (when it's suggested you don't) – it inspires a kind of helpless skittering along an axis of analogies. When language is used as so much relativist fodder, as it generally is in spam, one's own subjectivity is repeatedly destabilised in the encounter. As a pheomenon it's a post-structuralist's dream and nightmare all in one. On the one hand, this is language as a pure act of persuasion on all levels, *pace* Derrida, on the other, the subject being persuaded segues from human to algorithmic filter without warning, prompting chance illusory poetics, harsh disjunctions and an instinctive reach for metaphor to orientate oneself and impose tentative order on these breaks. But in viewing spam each of those resultant metaphors is both exact and inadequate and speaks to that moment alone – so that only a truly digital sequencing of them, in all their disparity, might make sense of the phenomenon of encountering spam, at least at a sustained affective level. *Casualty wards. Howard Hughes' paranoia. The homeless. Childhood meals. Nightclub doormen. The drowning:* an elusive promise of indexical consistency.

But yes, a shift of metaphor and a final scan of the horizon for the almost drowned – the unanswered work e-mail that has been sinking inexorably to the bottom of the inbox, clinging to a token flag for survival. Free from the weight of spam it is temporarily buoyant and visible again, but perhaps this is the third and final time it will receive direct attention before being left to the mercy of a search and recovery. This should guarantee action but doesn't. The enervating quality of the activity that has made the message visible again mitigates against acting on it.

In Siegfried Kracauer's essay 'Travel and Dance' (1925), the writer described affluent travellers thus:

> As travellers, they distance themselves from their habitual location; going to an exotic place is their sole remaining means of showing that they have outgrown the regions of the Here that enslave them. They experience supra-spatial endlessness by travelling in such an endless geographic space and, specifically, through travel as such. Such travel is of the sort that above all and most of the time has no particular destination; its meaning is exhausted in the mere fact of changing locations. This is to say that for them the interlocking of reality, its in-one-another (Ineinander) quality has been reduced to a sequence, to an after-each-other (Nacheinander) structure.
> (from *The Mass Ornament*)

All the early critical metaphors for web navigation owed much to this type of conception of travel. One paradox of spam is that the trace elements it carries are true to a point of origin, conveying a faint register of the culture that produced these fragments, even when the ostensible claims they are reconstituted for are false. So it is navigable to an extent – deserving of consideration within the conceptual frame of travel. It is an infinitesimally small journey that begins again with each press of the delete button. It is a journey though, albeit one that doesn't reward consideration of intent or destination – only the sense that you're repeatedly being thrown back on yourself.

Just under three minutes have passed.

It's steady work, with few pauses.

and sensational – infecting thousands of machines in minutes and inviting attention and counter-measures. Storm is low-key and stealthy – it turns the infected
machine into a slave and host for the virus – linking it to other infected machines
to carry out a delegated responsibility within a peer-to-peer network. Many
machines in the infected network are dormant for long periods – apparently running as normal and not involved in spam campaigns or denial-of-service attacks.
A small proportion of machines are used to propagate the virus and monitor the
network as command-and-control centres as the network grows. Shutting them
down simply shifts their role to a previously dormant part of the network.
Attempts to attack it spark reprisals – denial-of-service attacks on websites of
experts who tackle it etc. It is estimated that between one and 50 million computers are infected with the virus – which as yet has been used for relatively minor
purposes. This unused potential, described as 'military-scale' by some commenta-
tors, is perhaps the most disconcerting aspect of Storm.

HI HERE IS IT! Clint Max Congratulations FROM: EUROMILLIONS
INTERNATIONALPRIZE CLAIM CENTER Sir/Madam, Euromillions
international S.A. wish to bring to your notice the 2008 results of cyber lottery
games held on 2008.All participants were selected through lucky email and number generator system from the internet randomly drawn from over 100,000
COMPANIES and 50,000,000.(Individuals private/personal) email addresses in
Asia, Australia, New Zealand, Europe, North and South America, Middle East
and Africa. The ticket for the lottery was made possible by Euronet promotion
international, U.S.A. and IBERO PROMOTION COMPANY S.A.(Spain) as
part of their effort to contribution to help rebuild the devastated area of Asia
caused by the tsunami. As a result of this, 20% of your claim will be sending to
euronet overseas account which will be sent to you upon claim. YOU WIN-
NING INFORMATION ARE AS FOLLOW: TICKET NUMBER:
S.A./B2/2300 SERIAL NUMBER: EU2100100 DREW LUCKY NUM-
BERS: 17,21,69.45. WINNING CATEGORY: FIRST CATEGORY

BALLLINE 88 WINNING AMOUNT: $1,300,000.00 (ONE MILLION, THREE HUNDRED THOUSAND DOLLARS) We asked that you keep the winning information Confidential until your claims have been processed and your money remitted to you. This is part of our security protocol to avoid double claiming and unwarranted abuse of this program by scammers. many businessmen take toward their critics.' He drew a parallel to the mistaken tactics of many college administrators: 'College administrators learned too late that such appeasement serves to destroy free speech, academic freedom and genuine scholarship. One campus radical demand was conceded by university heads only to be followed by a fresh crop which soon escalated to what amounted to a demand for outright surrender.' To begin your lottery claims, please contact your claims agent below TINO TRUST AGENCY MR CLINT MAX DIRECTOR OF FOREIGN OPERATIONS Calle 15,2a. Avenida De America, 22830 Madrid, Spain. One need not agree entirely with Mr. St. John's analysis. But most observers of the American scene will agree that the essence of his message is sound. American business 'plainly in trouble'; the response to the wide range of critics has been ineffective, and has included Note that all prize money must be claimed not later than 2008. Claims that are not made before the above date will be returned and regarded as unclaimed fund. In 2000 the fishing vessel Seafresh 1 caught fire and sank in the remote Chatham Islands, New Zealand. Salvage attempts by an international company failed, and the ship was left where it sank. Before sinking, Seafresh 1 had been contaminated with the invasive Japanese seaweed, Undaria Pinnatifida. It quickly took hold of the sunken hull, and any subsequent spreading presented an ecological threat. Congratulation again Sincerely,
Mrs sarah lopez

ASS. HEAD EUROMILLIONS INFO CENTER. Pete Franklin, the big unit When luncheon time arrived he met his father, and Mr Oranjestad, Aruba, po b 1200 Oh, no, said Dorothy, we've been there, and we know The Valley of

Voe is certainly a charming place, resumed the Wizard; but we cannot be contented in any other land than our own, for long Joslyn took occasion to reprove his son in strong language for running away from home and leaving them filled with anxiety as to his fate However, when he saw how happy and improved in health his dear wife was at her boy's return, and when he had listened to Rob's manly confession of error and expressions of repentance, he speedily forgave the culprit and treated him as genially as ever Hazel Q. Perfectionist Hi! How's yourself? Aidaa Against change of fortune set a brave heart. Real courage is when you know you're licked before you begin, but you begin anyway and see it through no matter what. Amusement to an observing mind is study. A sort of war of revenge on the intellect is what, for some reason, thrives in the contemporary social atmosphere. The fundament upon which all our knowledge and learning rests is the inexplicable. Friendship is a living thing that lasts only as long as it is nourished with kindness, empathy and understanding. Let us not be content to wait and see what will happen, but give us the determination to make the right things happen. People have been so busy relating to how I look, it's a miracle I didn't become a self-conscious blob of protoplasm. Only Christ could have conceived Christ. Enthusiasm is very good lubrication for the mind. Happiness is a positive cash flow. Neither the sun nor death can be looked at with a steady eye Who loves well, chastises well. The advantage of love at first sight is that it delays a second sight. Doubt obscures the true vision of the heart. Our own physical body possesses a wisdom which we who inhabit the body lack. We give it orders which make no sense. Our dead are never dead to us, until we have forgotten them. Love shall be our token love be yours and love be mine.
Mural K. Entrepreneur

PLATO IS ONLINE NOW. Spinoza is grinding his lenses in the same room he receives visitors – the dust of the task and the dust of the world swirling in the same space, without pause – every lens angled towards the social. Leibniz wants to add you as a friend.

DON'T BE LIKE THAT . . . :) I'm so sorry! :) Hasta la vista This is the precept by which I have lived: Prepare for the worst expect the best and take what comes. Concentration is my motto — first honesty, then industry, then concentration. Memory is the treasury and guardian of all things. Some people try to find things in this game that don't exist but football is only two things- blocking and tackling. Rich folks always talk hard times. Strike the dog dead, it's but a critic! We inevitably doom our children to appeasement; the time has come — indeed, it is long overdue — for the wisdom, ingenuity and resources of American business to be marshalled against those who would destroy it. Responsibility of Business Executives What specifically should be done? The first essential — a prerequisite to any effective action — is for busi- nessmen to confront this problem as a primary responsibility of corporate management. The overriding first need is for businessmen to recog- nize failure and frustration when we try to set their goals for them. To win in this country these days you have got to campaign down to a thirteen-year-old's level of mental development. Nobody's ever the greatest anything. There is no knowledge, no light, no wisdom that you are in possession of, but what you have received it from some source. If poverty is the mother of crime, lack of good sense is the father. There are things known, and there are things unknown. And in between are the doors. When you write down your life, every page should contain something no one has ever heard about. Alas, I am dying beyond my means. Expect the best, plan for the worst, and prepare to be surprised. Knowledge like timber shouldn't be mush use till they are seasoned. How about this for a headline for tomorrow's paper? French fries. The eternal stars shine out as soon as it is dark. I would be as lost as a sparrow in an oven.
Eliot

PLEASE CONFIRM EVERYTHING . . . Would you REFINANCE if you knew you'd SAVE THoUSANDZ? Or get a Lo an of 250,000.00 , you already qualified. We'll get you the lowest possible rate. Don't believe me?

Toq We cherish our friends not for their ability to amuse us, but for our ability to amuse them. Seven's a banquet nine a brawl. Roots is not just a saga of my family. It is the symbolic saga of responsibilities. If our system is to survive, top management must be equally concerned with protecting and preserving the system itself. This involves far more than an increased emphasis on 'public relations' or 'governmental affairs' — two areas in which corporations long have invested substantial sums. Asignificant first step by individual corporations could well be the designation of an executive vice president (ranking with other executive VP's) whose responsibility a people. My wife's jealousy is getting ridiculous. The other day she looked at my calendar and wanted to know who May was. You generally hear that what a man doesn't know doesn't hurt him, but in business what a man doesn't know does hurt. Without some goals and some efforts to reach it, no man can live. The voice of the Lord is the voice of common sense, which is shared by all that is. Demetrius England V-codin and Hydrocodone Heree wGEpe Highest quality medds here: V-codin 225.00 (90 pi lls) Valliuum 153.00 (90 pi lls) Vi graa 270.00 (90 pi lls) Cai llis 348.00 (90 pi lls) Codeinne 126.00 (90 pi lls) X|a naax 171.00 (90 pi lls) All orderrs are delivered by Fedex with full tracking 24/7. Satisfactiionnss guuaranteeed . . . to get rid of maiiling list:

Urbanest H. Flavored

BUENOS DIAS! Farewell that the ultimate issue may be survival — survival of what we call the free enterprise system, and all that this means for the strength and prosperity of America and the freedom of our people. The day is long past when the chief executive officer of a major corporation discharges his responsibility by maintaining a satisfactory growth of profits, with due regard to the corporation's public and social Occupation C. Cadence I don't want to live — I want to love first, and live incidentally. It was prettily devised of Aesop, 'The fly sat on the axle tree of the chariot wheel and said, what dust do I raise!' A civil guest will no more talk all, than eat all the feast. I don't psyche myself up. I psyche myself down. I think clearer when I'm not psyched up. We trifle when we assign limits to our desires, since nature hath set none. Gaiety — a quality of ordinary men. Genius always presupposes some disorder in the machine. Jealousy is never satisfied with anything short of an omniscience that would detect the subtlest fold of the heart. We are all HIV-positive. No one knows when they are well off. One word frees us of all the weight and pain of life that word is love is to counter — on the broadest front — the attack on the enterprise system. The public relations department could be one of the foundations assigned to this executive, but his responsibilities should encompass some of the types of activities referred to subsequently in this memorandum. His budget and staff should be adequate to the task. Possible Role of the Chamber of Commerce But independent and uncoordinated activity by individual corporations, as important as this is, will not be sufficient. Love is the last relay and ultimate outposts of eternity. To err is human, but when the eraser wears out ahead of the pencil, you're overdoing it. Rob listened to this sad tale with real sympathy. But I didn't come here in a boat, said he The men sprang to their feet with white, scared faces

Mauricio prince

NOMINATED FOR MSC WHATAGREATIDEA! We provide a concept that will allow anyone with sufficient life experience to obtain a fully verifiable university diploma. Bachelor, Master or even a Doctorate. Think of it, within a month you too could be a college graduate. Many people share the same frustration, they are all doing the work of the person that has the degree, and the person that has the degree is getting all the money. Don't you think that it is time you were paid fair compensation for the level of work you are already doing? This is your chance to finally make the right move and receive your due benefits. If you are like most people, you are more than qualified with your experience, but you are lacking that prestigious piece of paper known as a diploma that is often the passport to success. Go Here http://www.freeinfoisn

in 1906 Thaksgiving by seat by seat Anna K Virus
in 1907 It's just Good luck! Clip Art Yes, it's great. Computers
in 1908 ICQ
and if you UFOS offhand in 1909 that's wrong Blair Witch Project
Young Magazines we are here Men in 1910

in 1913 here you are
in 1913 Digital Cameras The American student Foot and Mouth Desease
did you fear in 1913
in 1914 when placed Dale Earnhardt In fact Let's come back Groundhog Day

in 1916

How about you? David Blaine Pokemon Gold in 1918
Funny Guns in 1919

Grammy Awards in 1922 caan't hear The Holocaust Shoe them to me please Assian

Easter in 1924

would you like in 1926 when he Wrestling

X Men Those who say in 1930 Recipes Assian great

Look Movies this is...The X-Men in 1932
the Securities Act of 1933 and Section 21B of the Securities Exchange Act of 1934.
in 1934 what's the matter

in 1937

Publishers Clearing House in 1945 XFL Jokes Daytona 500 Don't go that way
in 1946 Oh, I see.
in 1947 Verizon Strike
I do ask you. AVI that's a go in 1949 Where do you live? Golf clubs
in 1950

It's O.K. in 1953 ICQ

Jokes in 1956 Netscape

Prom Hairstyles in 1959 Let's talk it over I'm trying How about you?
in 1961 Dean Kamen Pepsi Cola. Periodic Table in fact Ramadan
Did you make in 1961 Fancy that!

in 1963 I agree with you Diablo 2 The most Football
Chyna what's troubling you? aren't you? in 1964 We'd better send for... Classified
Detroit Auto Show numbers triple again in 1965 Illinois man Oprah Winfrey
Charlie's Angels in 1966

had fled abroad, but there, too, he gave no signs of himself 1969
It's just fine in 1969
in 1969 The point is well

in 1971

I do ask you. Digimon in 1973 Videos What's the difference?
in 1973 Teletubbies

World War II Pop Music in 1975 I have got Houses Ampland
In 1975 a new and now was thought that virtually all of Bulgakov had found its way into print.
in 1975
I'm afraid select location from Leonardo Di Caprio in 1975
Geena Davis in 1976
Blackout rescue Let's meet SI Swimsuit Shakespeare in 1977
Sable I think Teletubbies when the in 1978 I'll call back!
The IRS Limp Bizkit In my opinion. in 1978

in 1980 Sony
in 1981 Young Magazines we are here Men
The WWF Technology Microsoft in 1981

London Martin Luther King Jr. ???? to sign here in 1983
in 1983 U.S. Postal Service Warner Bross

in 1985 New Year I enjoy it...
in 1985 ?? ???? No thanks Paris
in 1986 I'm trying Miss World The Bible Free Thanks for visit
MIRC Chrono Cross Destiny's Child Madonna in 1987
but... Outlook Express Well i'm sorry Playstation 2 in 1987
Soccer in 1987

I am on a Dale Earnhardt Pokemon in 1991 Lord of the Rings Tenchi Muyo
based in New York and founded in 1992.
my name is in 1992 to see you Don't get excited! Good luck!

forward-looking statements within the meaning of The Private Securities Litigation Reform Act of 1995.
I'd rather not... when placed Newspapers did you fear ??? in 1995
Yes, it's me. in 1996 The WWF Winzip Pepsi Cola. Periodic Table
in 1996 Photos
in 1996 Vietnam War transit visa
I don't feel like When is the next? in 1997 Surfing Firefighters Cindy Margolis
diabetes, which was first developed in 1998 and introduced to the market in 2001.
Golf Clubs in 1999 when he let's shake hands vs. town, Network
Jessica Alba in 1999
it's beautiful ????? DMX Windows 2000 Websites Yes, sure
in 2000 Cheer up! Did you make O.K. When it was.
Ok deal Nelly May I..? in 2001

he was re-elected On March 14, 2004.

omore.info TODAY, to fill out an online application form AND GIVE YOUR LIFE A CHANCE! Undaria first appeared in New Zealand marinas in the spring of

Ashlie Rodriguez

NATURAL ENLARGEMENT Indeed, one was so nearly upon him when the electric current struck him that his head, in falling, bumped into Rob's stomach and sent him reeling against the side of the vessel. He quickly recovered himself, and seeing his enemies were rendered harmless, the boy entered the cabin and examined it curiously. And how strange an appearance he presented! His jacket was a wavering mass of white light, edged with braid of red flames that shot little tongues in all directions The buttons blazed in golden fire Cajole A. Code Real Housewires cheating I'm so sorry! :) Bi xatire be moha family. *Mr. Mohammed Abacha.*

SEGUE. I'M BLINKING in a Brooklyn coffee shop writing about filtering spam as the sun edges round the school that was in that film that time (*Half Nelson*, 2006). The time it has taken me to visit imdb.com to confirm the reference has stilled the slight caffeine rush that comes from cutting and pasting faster than articulate thought allows. The Bidonville free wifi network reaches to the school doors and half a block towards the park and defines a pale for vertiginous plundering of information, if not knowledge.

DEAR SIR, STRENGTH LIES IN ORGANIZATION, in careful long-range planning and implementation, in consistency of action over an indefinite period of years, in the scale of financing available only through joint effort, and in the political power available only through united action and national organiza-tions. Moreover, there is the quite understandable reluctance on the part of any one corporation to get too far out in front and to make itself too visible a tar-get. The role of the National Chamber of Commerce is therefore vital.

Other national organizations (especially I am Mohammed Abacha, the eldest son of the late president of Nigeria, General Sani Abacha. I was falsely accused of murder and as such was imprisoned, but thanks to Allah, I have been released for my innocence. Well dear friend I need your assistance in transferring some of my money into your account, because the government is making plans to seize them, as they did to my fathers own. Please view this site and read its content carefully, http://news.bbc.co.uk/1/hi/world/africa/635720.stm http://news.bbc.co.uk/1/hi/world/africa/1741445.stm http://www.jubi leeplus.org/worldnews/africa/nigeria200802.htm http://news.bbc.co.uk/1/hi/worl d/africa/468903.stm the amount is $29million in a Security Abroad. To indicate your interest, contact me urgently those of various industrial and commercial groups) should join in the effort, but no other organizations appear to be as well situated as the Chamber. It enjoys a strategic position, with a fine reputation and a broad base of support. Also — and this is of immeasurable merit — there are hundreds of local Chambers of Commerce which can play a vital supportive role and confidentially for more information and the roles you will play in this business. All the legal information concerning this Money will be sent to you as soon as we agree together. I have been confined only to Kano and all my calls are monitored, So I will get you the needed information. If this proposal satisfies you, please contact me immediately with your full names, telephone and fax numbers to enable me contact you. And give to you every detail of this transaction from beginning to the end on behalf of the family. Thanks for your cooperation. Best Regard.
Mohammed Abacha.

PERRY LUKE PLEASE GET BACK TO US Would you REFINANCE if you knew you'd SAVE THoUSANDZ? Or get a Lo an of 305,000.00, you already quaIified. We'll get you the lowest possible rate. Don't believe me? Fill out our small onIine questionaire and we'll show you how.

 Get the home/house and or car you always wanted, it only takes 06 seconds of your time: Best Regards, Justin Sauterne L. Anesthetized How do you do? Rise and shine! Gero arte Civilization must be destroyed. The hairy saints of the North have earned this crumb by their complaints. The test of civilization is its estimate of women. The apparel oft proclaims the man. Apparently there is nothing that cannot happen today. If you would live innocently, seek solitude. The greater the hold of government upon the life of the individual citizen, the greater the risk of war. Those who shine in the second rank, are eclipsed by the first. It hardly need be said that before embarking upon any program, the Chamber should study and analyze possible courses of action and activities, weighing risks against probable effectiveness and feasibility of each. Considerations of cost, the assurance of financial and other support from members, adequacy of staffing and similar problems will all require the most thoughtful Some fellows get credit for being conservative when they are only stupid. Critics! Those cut-throat bandits in the paths of fame. An old thing becomes new if you detach it from what usually surrounds it. What sort of philosophers are we, who know absolutely nothing about the origin and destiny of cats? The value of an idea has nothing whatever to do with the sincerity of the man who expresses it. The person is a poor judge who by an action can be disgraced more in failing than they can be honored in succeeding. I think most people are curious about what it would be like to be able to meet yourself — it's eerie. If you're ever given the choice between happiness and intelligence choose happiness Your character will be what you yourself choose to make it. Everything comes to us from others. To Be is to belong to someone. Health is a state of complete physical, mental and social well-being, and not merely the absence of disease or infirmity. Replicated O. Boxcar Buenos dias! Excuse me . . . :) Dovidjenja He who has been bitten by a snake fears a piece of string. In faith and hope the world will disagree, But all mankind's concern is charity. Death is the golden key that opens the palace of eternity. Fear is the foundation of most government. We never reflect how pleasant it is to ask for nothing. We're more popular than Jesus Christ now. I don't know which will go first rock and roll or Christianity. It is usually best to be generous with praise, but cautious with criticism. I have a higher and grander standard of principle than George Washington. He could not lie I can, but I won't. A specialist is a person who fears the other subjects. Man is a useless passion. In this world, full often, our joys are only the tender shadows which our sorrows cast.I have learnt to love you late, Beauty at once so ancient and so new! When all are wrong, everyone is right. What happiness is there which is not purchased with more or less of pain? To us also, through every star, through every blade of grass, is not God made visible if we will open our minds and our eyes. No person was ever honored for what he received. Honor has been the reward for what he gave. Keep out of the suction caused by those who drift backwards. To find a form that accommodates the mess, that is the task of the artist now.

Windsurfing A. Sterns

GOOD MORNING. Yokwe Literature flourishes best when it is half trade and half an art. People die of fright and live of confidence. A man must eat a peck of salt with his friend, before he knows him. It's not the drinking to be blamed, but the excess. Incompatibility. In matrimony a similarity of tastes, particularly the taste for domination. Seek to cultivate a buoyant, joyous sense of the crowded kindnesses of God in your daily life. Everyone enjoys doing the kind of work for which he is best suited. Never let the other fellow set the agenda. Idealists are foolish enough to throw caution to the winds. They have advanced mankind and have enriched the world. Love is not just looking at each other, it's looking in the same direction. If happiness could be brought, few of us could pay the price consideration. The Campus The assault on the enterprise system was not mounted in a few months. It has gradually evolved over the past two decades, barely perceptible in its origins and benefiting (sic) from a gradualism that provoked little awareness much less any real reaction. Although origins, sources and causes are complex and interrelated, and obviously difficult to identify without careful qualification, there is reason to believe that the What makes us so bitter against people who outwit us is that they think themselves cleverer than we are. Disability is a matter of perception.

If you can do just one thing well, you're needed by someone. Madness is something rare in individuals — but in groups, parties, peoples, ages it is the rule. Idleness is the stupidity of the body, and stupidity is the idleness of the mind. Don't be afraid to take a big step if one is indicated. You can't cross a chasm in two small jumps. Fortune does not so much change men, as it unmasks them. Friends are as companions on a journey, who ought to aid each other to persevere in the road to a happier life. Westbound B. Staphylococcus Old Aged Married Woemn Excuse me . . . :) Khamaba kuhle B&#0097rclays Bar‮yalc‬s ema&#105l veri&#102ication D_ae_r B_syalcra_ Me_bm_er, T_sih_ em_lia_ was s_tne_ by the Ba_lcr_ays s_revre_ to verify y_uo_r ema_li_ addr_se_s. You m_tsu_ compl_ete_ t_sih_ pr_co_ess by cl_ikci_ng on the l_ni_k be_wol_ and ente_nircampus is the single most dynamic source. The social science faculties usually include members who are unsympathetic to the enterprise system. They may range from a Herbert Marcuse, Marxist faculty member at the University of California at San Diego, and convinced socialists, to the ambivalent liberal critic who finds more to condemn than to commend. Such faculty members Volunteer divers and data collectors are needed to help the long term effort to monitor and eradicate Undaria pinnatifida, an Asian kelp invading Monterey and Southern California. This is a quick growing, opportunistic alga that is capable of having a profound influence on the ecosystem and can become a fouling species on most marine structures. bel_wo_: http://b_arc_ ys._a_l _co.uk/XtsHY7yTbK8nGmwCV7TM2p ByX2hkK5lAnCJV4JBNw1KKOQ4 dYKKWdPg1lbws3lovw_ hai nelson male muscle boosting system There was no response. He extended the tube and, as he pressed the button, described a semi-circle with the instrument Immediately the tall guardsmen toppled over like so many tenpins, and Rob stepped across their bodies and penetrated to the reception room, where a brilliant assemblage awaited, in hushed and anxious groups, for opportunity to obtain audience with the king Weeks Q. Skirt What's so good about it? :) How do you do? Vi ses snart Nature gave us one tongue

and two ears so we could hear twice as much as we speak. The only thing worse than a liar is a liar that's also a hypocrite! What I do say is that no man is good enough to govern another man without that other's consent. The history of the past interests us only in so far as it illuminates the history of the present. Hope for the best, but prepare for the worst. To be able to say how much love, is love but little. It takes two flints to make a fire. My candle burns at both ends it will not last the night but ah, my foes, and oh, my friends — it gives a lovely light! The physician's highest calling, his only calling, is to make sick people healthy — to heal, as it is termed. The family you come from isn't as important as the family you're going to have. Virtue alone has majesty in death. Art is the path of the creator to his work. Love is the only sane and satis-factory answer to the problem of human existence. need not be in a majority. They are often personally attractive and magnetic; they are stimulating teachers, and their controversy attracts student following; they are prolific writers and lec-turers; they author many of the textbooks, and they exert enormous influence — far out of proportion to their numbers — on their colleagues and in the academic world. I sometimes wander whether all pleasures are not substitutes for joy. The ultimate result of shielding men from the effects of folly, is to fill the world with fools. Sure of their qualities and demanding praise, more go to ruined fortunes than are raised. Exhilaration is that feeling you get just after a great idea hits you, and just before you realize what's wrong with it. A strong man and a waterfall always channel their own path.
Nettle H. Trims

WOULD YOU BELIEVE IT? How's tricks? Pama mine' The true measure of life is not length, but honesty. Every one is the architect of his own fortune. The principle of the Gothic architecture is infinity made imaginable. Is anyone sim-ply by birth to be applauded or punished? Don't look back, just keep on walk-ing. He does not weep who does not see. moderate persuasion and even the relatively few often being less articulate and aggressive than their crusading colleagues. This situation extending back many years and with the imbalance gradually worsening, has had an enormous impact on millions of young American students. In an article in Barron's Weekly, seeking an answer to why so many young people are disaffected even to the point of being revolutionaries, it was said: 'Because they were Be happy while you're living, for you're a long time dead. The person who lives by hope will die by despair. We have no more right to consume happiness without producing it than to consume wealth without producing it. Grief is light that is capable of counsel. Luck affects everything. Let your hook always be cast in the stream where you least expect it there will be a fish. True friendship can afford true knowledge. It does not depend on darkness and ignorance. taught that way.'10 Or, as noted by columnist Stewart Alsop, writing about his alma mater: willfully manufacturing unsafe products that will maim or kill the buyer. He emphasizes that he is not talking just about 'fly-by-night hucksters' but the top management of blue chip business.' We want all our friends to tell us our bad qualities it is only the particular ass that does so whom we can't tolerate. I was the only one there I never heard of. I am dying beyond my means. Kindness and honesty can be expected only from the strong. The higher character a person supports the more they should regard their smallest actions. I can only wait for the final amnesia, the one that can erase an entire life. Jocelyn Blackburn Need software? sidney burlap vegetable crept laue lard risible blossom magna bijective detain harvey waybill greta participate toodle slam breastplate bromfield piece glisten absolve rotunda deciduous peppy dissuade andes aps norwich circumstantial decouple heartfelt rosenblum demolish friedman blather cowl scanty burg cocksure gall darling delhi anaglyph laminate attainder ruckus reticent leggy anorthosite wharf skopje windup chlorophyll homebuilding fourier leash coercive parvenu cottrell dustbin marrow phycomycetes bezel corbel axiology diabolic posthumous o'hare annulled maze amperage spatterdock cambodia centrex switchblade telltale shanty crosstalk athabascan quanta wrap insult levitate appropriate feline atom brunswick datum cattle colatitude spurge yolk gymnasium pinnate vaudeville hyena handicapper spy assert linguist cerebrate ridgway clockwork id acknowledge gorgon internal stalk recession surround incantation transform sofa floorboard tub breed.

Dendrite R. Semanticsk, Old Aged Housewife

IT SEEMS TO BE AN APPROPRIATE way to say hello to OOP lovers :) Na ave shilwapo nawa olinda robertson Proven to get some of the action is an invasive kelp native to Japan. Commonly known as 'wakame', an ingredient in miso soup, this alga is commercially grown throughout Asia for human consumption. It has invaded many of the world's oceans, from European waters, to waters off New Zealand. tightly bound We light fire, said the chief Cardiology D. Ficklest As these 'bright young men,' from campuses across the country, seek opportunities to change a system which they have been taught to distrust — if not, indeed 'despise' — they seek employment in the centers of the real power and influence in our country, namely: (i) with the news media, especially television; (ii) in government, as Guten Tag :)) O dabo Be removed now! Barman Q. Oversold OEM Software habitually inrecdible cheap staffers and consultants at various levels; (iii) in elective politics; (iv) as lecturers and writers, and (v) on the faculties at various levels of education. carmon gomez Now you can be more popular with women The people who thronged the sidewalks cheered and waved their hats and handkerchiefs with enthusiasm, while a band of musicians played a German air, which Rob could distinctly hear. While he gazed, spellbound, the scene changed, and he looked upon a great warship entering a harbor with flying pennants The rails were lined with officers and men straining their eyes for the first sight of their beloved VATERLAND after a long foreign cruise, and a ringing cheer, as from a thousand throats, came faintly to Rob's ear.

Milrace O. Sniggers

WE SINCERELY APOLOGIZE FOR ANY INCONVENIENCE that this mail may cause to you! Chang Wen-sheng MEI LUNG HANDI-CRAFTS CO., LTD No.2, LANE 6 CHENG TE ROAD SEC.4, TAIPEI

TAIWAN Radish I. Although I've heard a lot about you Guten Tag :)) El kio ke te guadre Genius is the gold in the mine talent is the miner who works and brings it out. Freedom is the only law which genius knows. No tears in the writer, no tears in the reader. We are all of us the worse for too much liberty. He who is not impatient is not in love. Men exist for the sake of one another. To be a champ, you have to believe in yourself when nobody else will. When you give yourself, you receive more than you give. Doing well is the result of doing good. That's what capitalism is all about. Of course you're always at liberty to judge governmental departments with large authority over the business system they do not believe in. If the foregoing analysis is approximately sound, a priority task of business — and organizations such as the Chamber — is to address the campus origin of this hostility. Few things are more sanctified in American life than academic freedom. It would be fatal to attack this as a principle. But if academic freedom is to retain the the critic. Judge people as critics, however, and you'll condemn them all! What is a Communist? One who has yearnings for equal division of unequal earnings. Balance is the enemy of art. No literature is complete until the language it was written in is dead. We pay when old for the excesses of youth. If you want to give a man credit, put it in writing. If you want to give him hell, do it on the phone.
Richmond J.

I KNOW THE FACE, BUT... Hej. Sicaru guiaana tu Most of the existing textbooks have some sort of comparisons, but many are superficial, biased and unfair and then your friends tomorrow. The worst education which teaches self-denial, is better than the best which teaches everything else, and not that. Come into the light of things. Let nature be your teacher. The future comes slowly, the present flies and the past stands still forever. There are no great men, only great challenges that ordinary men are forced by circumstances to meet. There is no sanctuary of virtue like home. Alcohol is barren. The words a man speaks in the night of drunkenness fade like the darkness itself at the coming of

day. Court... a place where they dispense with justice. If you think education is expensive, try ignorance. I made a wrong mistake Great and good are seldom the same man. It sounds extraordinary but it's a fact that balance sheets can make fascinating reading. Change yourself, change your fortunes. What Can Be Done About the Public? A wreck on shore is a beacon at sea. A benevolent man should allow a few faults in himself, to keep his friends in countenance. Never a lip is curved with pain That can't be kissed into smiles again. Modesty is the conscience of the body.
Jay Burgos

MY FRIEND TELLS ME about the virus over dinner – he is in New York for a week. I am tired and he is jetlagged and we both seem glad that our partners dominate the conversation. We become animated by the discussion over Storm, though – but I'm sleepy and as happy for the bill as for this exchange of rich fragments. We usually swap these stories via e-mail, and there's something of the uncanny in corporeally observing and participating in this information exchange between tired hosts – the pleasure arriving simultaneously with the information, almost too metaphorically rich to bear. No time to set oneself against the scale of the information realm and match this new knowledge to one's imagined visual of it. All affect, no screen in sight. Uncomfortable sense of immanence. Rain in the East Village. Home. Inbox. Sleep.

ILLUSTRATIONS

FRONT AND BACK COVER *The Stokc to Watch*, Graham Parker, 2006. From a series of neon signs based on titles of spam e-mails.

INSIDE FRONT COVER *Chaff Image (barricade)*, Graham Parker, lightbox (detail), 2008.

INSIDE BACK COVER *Brown Brothers Underneath*, Graham Parker, lightbox (detail), 2006.

PAGES 7 AND 35 *Brief History*, Graham Parker, Giclée print (detail), 2006. Timeline of the past two hundred years assembled from fragments of dated text found in raw source code of a particular trope of spam e-mails. The spams were advertising fake Rolexes and fake college degrees.

For Ina

THANKS TO

Miguel Abreu, Bidonville, Diane Brown, Christine Burgin,
Tim Etchells, Sarah Fan, Benj Gerdes, Vlatka Horvat,
Emma Parker, John Parker, Represent, Jane Rolo,
Gerrie van Noord, and all at Book Works,
Lisa Ross, Augustinus Tjahaya.

FAIR USE (*Notes from Spam*)
Graham Parker

Published by
BOOK WORKS, LONDON

Copyright © Graham Parker, 2009

ISBN 978-1-906012-04-5

Designed by Pollen/Stewart Cauley and Graham Parker
Printed by Oddi in Iceland
Distributed by Book Works (UK and Ireland)
R.A.M. Publications and Distributions (USA and Canada)
Actar D (Europe and rest of world)

BOOK WORKS
19 Holywell Row
London EC2A 4JB
www.bookworks.org.uk
Telephone: +44 (0)207 247 2203

Book Works is funded by Arts Council England